Dedicated to my children Aaliyah and Tiana

https://themonster-series.com

Illustrations by Bibi Hecher

Thanks to author Karen McMillan for her assistance with this project.

ISBN: 978-1-8382213-3-1

In collaboration with Duckling Publishing and Chrissy Metge Ltd.
www.ducklingpublishing.com
www.chrissymetge.com

Duckling
publishing

CLAUDIA
Story of Separation

DONIA YOUSSEF

Once there was a little girl named Claudia. She'd just turned ten years old and celebrated with her family and friends. What a wonderful birthday it was, too, with her mum, dad, and grandparents.

But a few days later, something happened. Something that made Claudia's heart hurt.

Mum and Dad sat her down in the family room. They looked very serious! Mum's eyes were red, and Dad had circles under his own eyes. Claudia wondered if something bad had happened.

'What's wrong?' she asked. 'You look like you've been crying.'

Mum and Dad turned to each other. Now they looked really sad. And then they turned back to Claudia and said, 'Sweetheart, we have to tell you something very important.'

That day, Claudia learned that her mum and dad were separating. But she didn't know what that meant.

'It means that we're going to take a break from each other," said Mum.

'A break? But why? Don't you love each other?'

Mum and Dad took Claudia's hands and squeezed. 'Sometimes, Claudia, even people who love each other need to take a break from one another. This happens to some Mums and Dads.'

Claudia shook her head. 'Do you want to take a break from me instead?'

Sometimes, we think that Mum and Dad split up because of us. But that is the furthest thing from the truth!

'Oh no, Claudia,' said Mum. 'Neither of us want that, ever! Right now, Mummy and Daddy are unhappy with one another. Not you. We aren't mad... not at you or each other. We just understand that sometimes adults need to live apart.'

Claudia took a deep breath. She really needed it! This was a lot of important stuff. 'My friend Kayla's parents got a divorce. That means they don't live with each other anymore and they aren't married! Is that what is happening?'

'Well,' said Dad, 'we don't know yet. That is why we are separating. We need space apart to think and listen to what's right in our hearts.'

Mum nodded. 'And remember, Claudia, our hearts are always so full of love for you.'

'So, it's not my fault?'

'No!' Mum and Dad said together. 'You are the person who makes us happiest, and we both will always love and take care of you.'

This made Claudia feel better, but she didn't know what was going to happen, and this made her a little worried.

Dad moved to another flat, and she visited him there. He had a
beautiful view of a park, a kitchen where they made dinner, and a big
television to watch movies.

At home, Claudia and Mum spent lots more time together. They worked in the garden, did homework together, and went for walks with the dog.

After a while, Claudia said, 'Mum, are you and Dad talking? Please, tell me the truth.'

Mum sat down with Claudia. 'Yes, we are, sweetheart. We talk every week, but right now, we need some space to think and feel. This is important for us, so we can decide if we want to stay together. And remember, we won't keep secrets from you.'

At Dad's house, Claudia sat down on the couch. 'Dad, is it Mum's fault that you left?'

Dad shook his head. 'No, Claudia, it's not your Mum's fault. Separating is something we both decided to do. It's nobody's fault. This is about our feelings, and when we decide, we will tell you right away what is happening.'

At school, Claudia talked to her friend, Kayla. 'Did you cry when your parents separated?'

Kayla said, 'I did! I cried a lot, but then, Mum and Dad told me everything would be okay and that they love me so much.'

Claudia sighed. 'But then they got divorced.'

'It's all right, Claudia,' said Kayla. And then she hugged Claudia. 'Sometimes, Mums and Dads can't live together anymore. My brother and I thought it was because of us, but then we saw how happy they were living apart.'

So, Claudia took a walk in the playground, watching the brightly coloured birds in the trees, the leaves rustling in the wind, and the other children playing. She thought about how unhappy both Mum and Dad were lately. They even yelled at each other sometimes.

'Maybe,' said Claudia, 'Mum and Dad would be happier apart. But how will I see both of them?'

That night, Claudia went to her mum and asked a question. 'If you or Dad decide to leave, will I ever see you again?'

Mum held Claudia tightly. 'Oh, Claudia, yes, you will. Don't ever worry about that. Neither of us is going to leave you, no matter what happens. You will see us just like you do now. Things might be a bit different, but Mum and Dad will always be there for you!'

And so, Claudia spent time with both Mum and Dad during their separation.

Mum and Dad told Claudia they loved her very, very much. That they would always be by her side, even if they were apart. This made Claudia feel safe, and she was able to talk about it with Kayla.

Some Mums and Dads get back together, like Claudia's Mum and Dad. And she was happy when they did. But others, like Kayla's Mum and Dad, get a divorce. Kayla's parents still love her and her brother with all their hearts, though.

'We live with Dad but see Mum every weekend!' said Kayla. 'And we see our grandparents, and sometimes we have family dinners together.'

Claudia thanked Kayla for being there for her.

'Remember, Claudia,' said Mum, 'sometimes things change, but many things stay the same.'

The one important thing is that Dad and Mum always told Claudia that whatever she was feeling was normal and okay.

Even though mummies and daddies go through hard times, they don't stop loving you. *And don't worry! Some things change, but many things will stay the same.*

Claudia: A Story of Separation is written to help children when their parents are going through a separation.

After I released my first book, *The Monster in Mummy*, a story about a family facing cancer, I became more involved with different charities and organisations. Other cancer survivors then started to contact me, telling me their own stories. I realised there is so much we as a society are not aware of, and many difficult things in life, like a major illness, separation and divorce, aren't discussed openly. *Claudia: A Story of Separation* will hopefully be a useful tool for families at this challenging time.

Donia Youssef, Author & Producer of *The Monster series*.

If your parents split up, don't worry. You are not alone.
There are many of us kids out there, and it's all right.
Even though it's hard sometimes, you are going to have many
happy times ahead of you. And remember, both your
parents still love you and want the best for you!

TINY ANGEL
Press

THE M🦉NSTER

ISBN 978-1-8382213-3-1
90000
9 781838 221331

How to Draw
Dwarves & Gnomes

Amit Offir